D1293520

For information regarding permission, please contact lulu@lavamediallc.com or 212-333-1006, 1755 Broadway, 8th Floor, New York, NY 10019.

ISBN 978-1-338-61162-5

Published by Scholastic Inc., 557 Broadway, New York, NY 10012, by arrangement with Lava Media, LLC.

12 11 10 9 8 7 6 5 4 3 2 1 19 20 21 22 23 24

Printed in the U.S.A. 40

First Scholastic printing, September 2019

Author: Jason Flom and Allison Flom
Illustrator: Sophie Corrigan

Lulu
is a Rhinoceros

By Jason Flom
with Allison Flom

Illustrated by
Sophie Corrigan

SCHOLASTIC INC.

Yes! I am Lulu.

What I am *not* is a bulldog.
In fact, I am not a dog at all.

Can you guess what I am?

I'm a
RHINOCEROS!

In my heart, I have thick gray rhino skin!
But what I really have is soft, fuzzy fur.

In my mind I have a tail that whips and twirls! But what I see is a little nub that wiggles when I'm happy.

But the only thing
I don't have yet,
that I really,
really want...

Is my rhino HORN.

Hi, I'm a rhinoceros

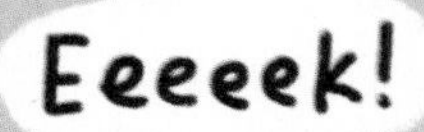
Eeeeek!

I'm a rhinoceros

Are you some kind of freak?

I'm a rhinoceros!

Do you think I can't see?

I. AM. A. RHINOCEROS!

You don't look like one to me!

If I only had my horn, they would finally see the REAL me!

Let's try this ice cream cone on for size! I think it would be a pretty cool horn...

Not cool...

COLD!

I don't think rhino horns
are supposed to be this floppy
... or stinky!

A traffic cone!
That might work...
WAHHH!
I CAN'T SEE
A THING!

I guess this banana will have to do...

Do YOU know who I am?
You're a bulldog. With a banana on your nose.

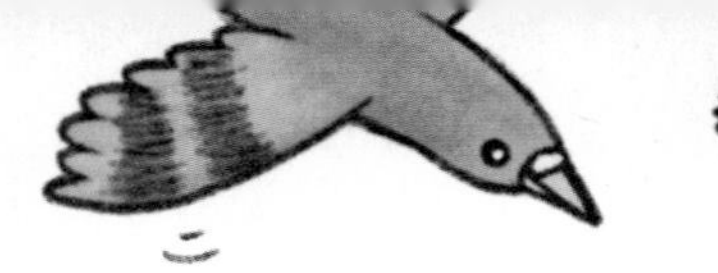

No, I'm a---
That's my HORN! I NEED that!

That's enough!
I've had it with pigeons!
I've had it with dogs!
I'VE HAD IT WITH
EVERYONE!

THAT'S MY HORN!
Beep! Beep!!
Beeeeep!!
IT'S A BANANA!
DON'T WALK
ZOO

GIVE ME BACK MY HORN!

NYC
ZOO
NO DOGS
ALLOWED
IT'S A
BANANA!!

It's my HORN, because I'm a RHINOCEROS!!
GIBBONS
elephants

!
SPLAT!
Keep OUT!
Rhino
Enclosure

YOINK!

You're a peculiar-looking rhino
Did you say "RHINO"?!
I AM a rhino!
How did you know?

We're in the rhinoceros enclosure.
So of course you're a rhino.

That's right - I am!
My name's Lulu, who are you?

I'm Flom Flom. I'm a tickbird.
Every rhino has a tickbird, and every tickbird has a rhino.

Well, I don't have a tickbird...

Well if you need me...
And if you need me...
THEN WHY DON'T WE...

Yes, I am Lulu.

I am a rhinoceros.

From the Author

This book is dedicated to my bulldog, Lulu, who spoils me with her unconditional love; to Ryan Tate and his band of heroes at VetPaw, who opened my eyes to the majesty of rhinos; to my parents, who taught me to stand up for what is right; and to my wonderful kids.

And thank you to Alex Gottlieb, Stefanie Gammill, Sophie Corrigan, Jenna Ruggiero, Devon O'Connor, Kelly Cutrone, and to my partners at Wicked Cow, Michael, Adam, and Matt.

Lulu is a Rhinoceros

By Jason Flom
with Allison Flom

Illustrated by
Sophie Corrigan

Lulu is a bulldog on the outside but a rhino on the inside.

Everyone thinks Lulu is a bulldog. It's what she looks like on the outside, so it *must* be what she is on the inside.

But Lulu knows she's not really a dog.

Lulu is a rhinoceros— that's what *she* sees when she looks in the mirror.

When Lulu decides to tell the world who she really is, a wild adventure begins.

This edition is available for distribution only through the school market.

SCHOLASTIC

www.scholastic.com

ISBN 978-1-338-61

9 781338 61